WITH JESUS
I Share

Copyrights

www.gnmkids.com

This book belongs to:

....

....

"I can't wait to go to the park!" Carlos exclaimed.
"I get to play with my new toy car."

When Carlos and Daddy got to the park, Carlos ran to the sandbox and started playing with his toy car. Maria, his neighbor, ran up to Carlos.

"No, you can't play with me! If I give you a turn, I'll never see how fast it can go," Carlos yelled.

"Come on! You've been playing with it this whole time," Maria yelled back.

On the way home, Carlos told
Daddy why he didn't let Maria
play with him.

"Did you know that a little boy gladly helped Jesus feed many people?" asked Daddy.

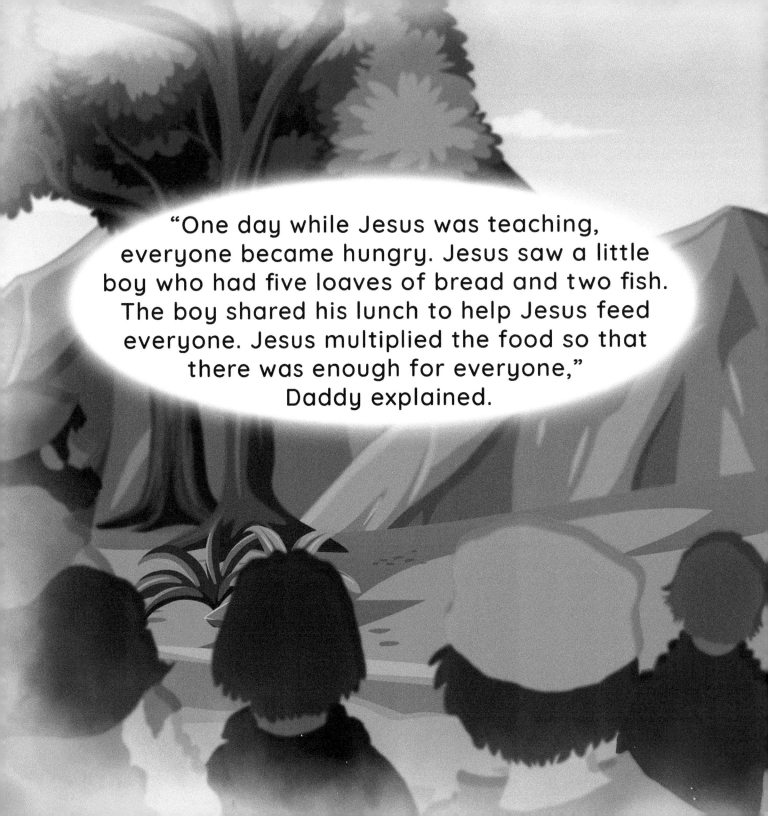

"One day while Jesus was teaching, everyone became hungry. Jesus saw a little boy who had five loaves of bread and two fish. The boy shared his lunch to help Jesus feed everyone. Jesus multiplied the food so that there was enough for everyone," Daddy explained.

"Wow! It was really kind of the boy to share his food," said Carlos.

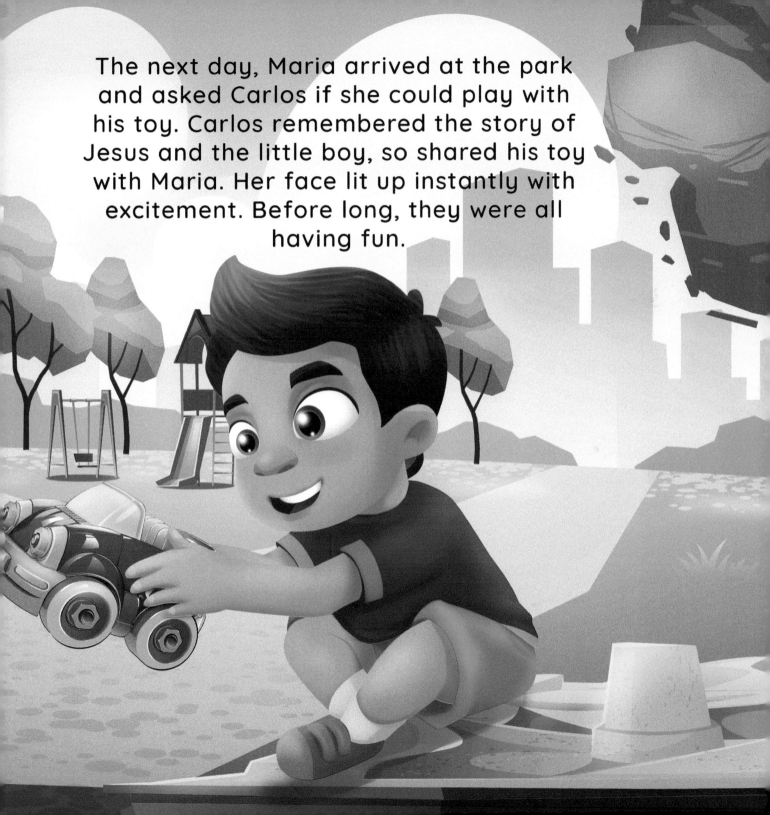

The next day, Maria arrived at the park and asked Carlos if she could play with his toy. Carlos remembered the story of Jesus and the little boy, so shared his toy with Maria. Her face lit up instantly with excitement. Before long, they were all having fun.

Daddy noticed and asked his son why he shared his toy.

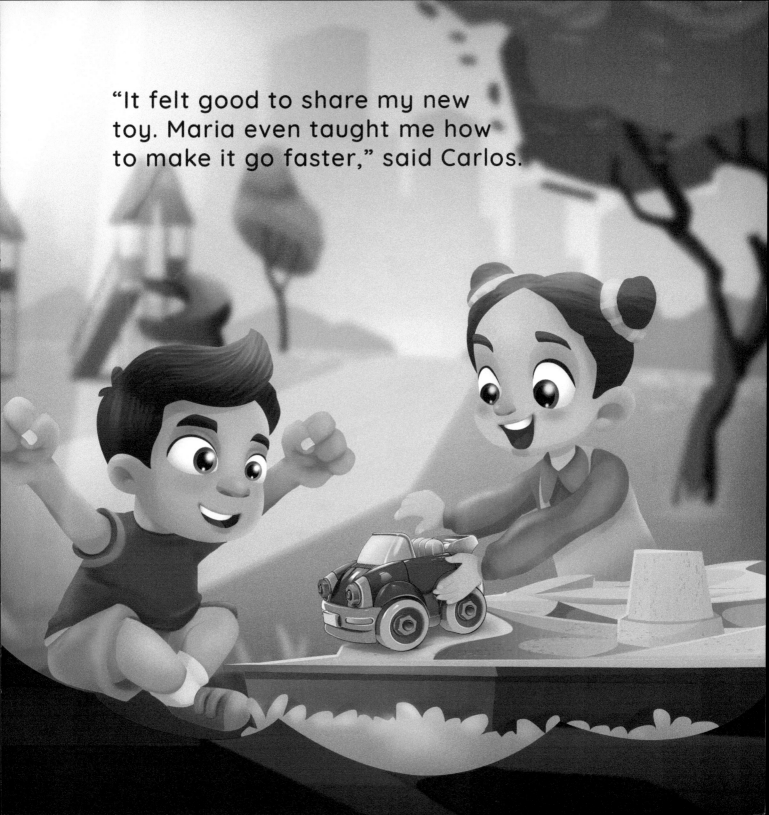

"It felt good to share my new toy. Maria even taught me how to make it go faster," said Carlos.

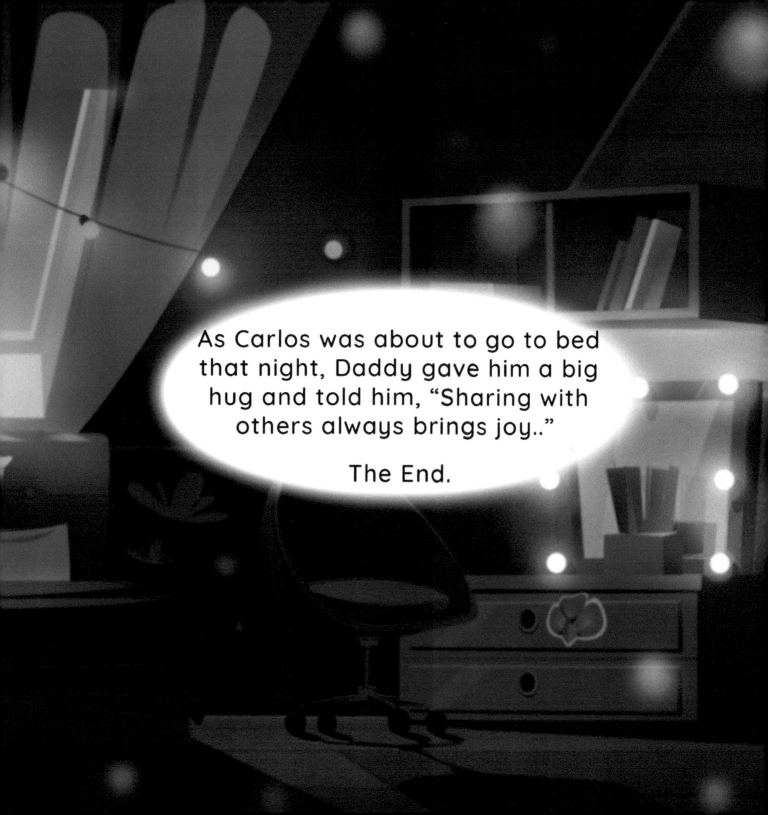

As Carlos was about to go to bed that night, Daddy gave him a big hug and told him, "Sharing with others always brings joy.."

The End.

"And do not forget to do good and to share with others, for with such sacrifices God is pleased"

Hebrews 13:16 NIV

Author's note:

Thank you so much for reading this book. If you enjoyed this book, we would love it if you could leave a review and recommend it to a friend.

If there is anything you would like to share with us to help us improve this book, please go to gnmkids.com/feedback

Please checkout our other books

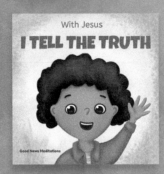

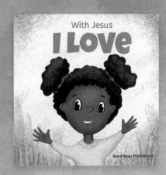

www.gnmkids.com